The Complete
PANCHATANTRA

Mitralabha Friendship and Gain

Retold & illustrated by
Bujjai

© Bujjai
First published 1999
Second impression June 2000

Published by
Devamala Books Pvt Ltd

III Floor Zenofer Tower
No 119/2 Jawaharlal Nehru Road
Jafferkhanpet
Chennai 600083
Phone 3711824 3711825
Fax 0091 44 3712332
e-mail msmgroup@satyam.net.in

Designed by Krishna Shastri
Processed by Bee Vee Graphics, Chennai
Printed by Vadapalani Press,
AVM Compound, Vadapalani, Chennai 600026

To Lakshmi, my wife,

Who, for forty years,

stood by me through my struggles,

encouraged me in all my endeavours,

and left me and my children

suddenly two years ago,

I dedicate these books

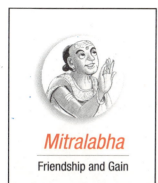

Mitralabha
Friendship and Gain

ONCE UPON A TIME, ON A BIG TREE IN A FOREST, LIVED A CROW NAMED LAGHUPATANAKA. ONE DAY, A HUNTER CAME THAT WAY...

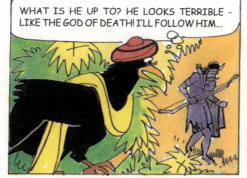

WHAT IS HE UP TO? HE LOOKS TERRIBLE - LIKE THE GOD OF DEATH! I'LL FOLLOW HIM...

I'LL SPREAD MY NET HERE...

MY GOD! I MUST WARN MY FRIENDS BEFORE IT'S TOO LATE!

LAGHUPATANAKA TOLD HIS FRIENDS ABOUT THE HUNTER AND ALL THE BIRDS FLEW AWAY. AFTER SOME TIME, CHITRAGRIVA, THE KING OF DOVES, AND HIS RETINUE CAME BY...

LOOK! LET US FLY DOWN AND EAT THAT GRAIN!

SOON AFTER, THE UNLUCKY DOVES WERE CAUGHT IN THE HUNTER'S NET.

ALAS! WE'VE BEEN TRICKED!

AHAHA! I AM LUCKY TODAY. WHAT A BIG COLLECTION OF BIRDS!

DON'T BE FRIGHTENED. LISTEN TO ME. NOW WE MUST ACT TOGETHER AND FLY OFF WITH THE NET.

NOW, GET READY! ONE...TWO.. THREE!

THEY HAVE FOOLED ME! I'LL FOLLOW THEM!

LAGHUPATANAKA FOLLOWED THE DOVES AND THE HUNTER...

LET'S SEE WHAT HE'LL DO!

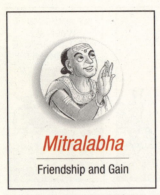

Mitralabha

Friendship and Gain

CHITRAGRIVA AND HIS FOLLOWERS FLEW AWAY WITH THE NET, THE HUNTER PURSUING THEM. LAGHUPATANAKA, THE CROW, FOLLOWED THEM, CURIOUS TO KNOW WHAT WOULD HAPPEN TO THE DOVES.

CAN THEY ELUDE THE HUNTER?

THEY'VE FOOLED ME BY STICKING TOGETHER. BUT THEY'LL SOON FALL OUT AND THEN I CAN NAB THEM!

THE BIRDS FLEW OVER HILL AND DALE AND THE HUNTER WAS EXHAUSTED.

OH! CAN'T FOLLOW THEM ANY LONGER...

EVEN MY NET IS LOST.

MY FRIENDS! THE DANGER IS PAST. THE HUNTER HAS TURNED BACK.

WHAT SHALL WE DO NOW?

HIRANYAKA, THE MOUSE, LIVES IN THAT TOWN. HE'S A FRIEND OF MINE. HE'LL FREE US FROM THIS NET. LET'S FLY THERE.

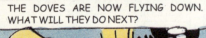

THE DOVES ARE NOW FLYING DOWN. WHAT WILL THEY DO NEXT?

AFTER SOME TIME...

HIRANYAKA! HIRANYAKA! PLEASE COME OUT, MY FRIEND!

WHO'RE YOU AND WHAT DO YOU WANT?

I'M YOUR FRIEND, CHITRAGRIVA, KING OF THE DOVES.

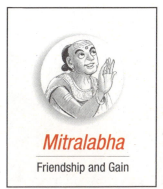

Mitralabha

Friendship and Gain

I'M YOUR FRIEND, CHITRAGRIVA, KING OF THE DOVES. PLEASE FREE US FROM THIS SNARE.

HIRANYAKA CAME OUT.

MY FRIEND, HOW DID IT HAPPEN?

I'LL TELL YOU BY AND BY... IT'S FATE!

ALL RIGHT, I SHALL FREE YOU FIRST. THE MASTER FIRST, THEN THE SERVANTS.

NO!

NO, NO, FREE MY FOLLOWERS FIRST. IT'S THE DUTY OF A KING TO LOOK TO THE WELFARE OF HIS SUBJECTS.

MY NOBLE FRIEND, I SHALL SET YOU ALL FREE.

LAGHUPATANAKA THE CROW WAS WATCHING THIS...

WONDERFUL! A REAL KING IS ONE WHO LOOKS AFTER HIS SUBJECTS AND HE ALONE IS A GENUINE FRIEND WHO HELPS IN TIMES OF DISTRESS.

HIRANYAKA SET HIS FRIEND AND THE OTHERS FREE.

HOW CAN WE THANK YOU, MY FRIEND!

WE MUST TAKE LEAVE OF YOU NOW.

I'LL MAKE FRIENDS WITH THIS NOBLE MOUSE.

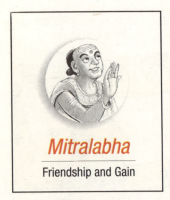

Mitralabha

Friendship and Gain

LAGHUPATANAKA APPROACHED HIRANYAKA'S HOUSE...

MY GOOD SIR, HIRANYAKA, PRAY COME OUT.

WHO IS IT?

I'M LAGHUPATANAKA, THE CROW. I'VE COME HERE SEEKING YOUR FRIENDSHIP.

A CROW AND A MOUSE? HOW CAN WE EVER BE FRIENDS? PLEASE LEAVE!

PRAY GRANT ME AN INTERVIEW.

I SEE NO GOOD IN OUR MEETING, PLEASE GO!

YOU'RE SO GOOD AND NOBLE. I SAW YOU FREEING CHITRAGRIVA AND HIS FOLLOWERS. PLEASE ACCEPT ME ALSO AS YOUR FRIEND.

NO. PLEASE GO!

IF YOU REFUSE, I'LL FAST UNTO DEATH AT YOUR DOOR.

MY GOOD FELLOW, THERE IS NO POSSIBILITY OF FRIENDSHIP BETWEEN US!

I DON'T SEE WHY NOT!

RIVAL WIVES, SAINT AND SINNER, LION AND ELEPHANT, WATER AND FIRE ARE NATURAL ENEMIES.

SO ALSO WE - A CROW AND A MOUSE.

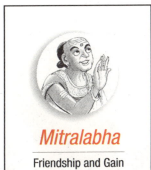

Mitralabha

Friendship and Gain

I DON'T AGREE WITH YOU, SIR! THERE IS NO PERSONAL ENMITY BETWEEN YOU AND ME. SO WHY CAN'T WE BE FRIENDS?

PLEASE! GO AWAY.

I ASSURE YOU OF MY SINCERITY. I'M PREPARED TO TAKE AN OATH ON IT.

I THINK I CAN BELIEVE HIM...

ALL RIGHT, MY DEAR FELLOW! FROM NOW ON, WE'RE FRIENDS.

THANK YOU!

SO THE MOUSE AND THE CROW LIVED TOGETHER IN FRIENDSHIP AND HELPED EACH OTHER. MANY DAYS PASSED. ONE DAY...

MY FRIEND HIRANYAKA! I'M NOT HAPPY HERE. I'VE DECIDED TO LEAVE THIS PLACE.

WHY?

THIS COUNTRY IS FAMINE-STRICKEN AND HUNGRY PEOPLE ARE SETTING TRAPS FOR BIRDS EVERY DAY.

THAT'S SAD. WHERE DO YOU WISH TO GO?

THERE'S A FOREST IN THE NORTH WITH A LAKE IN IT. THAT'S WHERE A FRIEND OF MINE, MANTHARA, LIVES. I ENJOY HIS COMPANY. I THINK I'LL GO THERE.

I, TOO, CAN'T LIVE HERE ANY LONGER...I'M ALSO UNHAPPY...

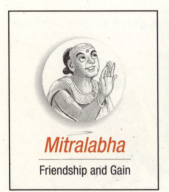

Mitralabha

Friendship and Gain

I'LL COME WITH YOU TO YOUR FRIEND'S PLACE.

HOW? YOU CAN'T FLY.

BUT YOU CAN CARRY ME ON YOUR BACK, MY FRIEND!

EXCELLENT IDEA!

LAGHUPATANAKA AND HIRANYAKA STARTED ON THEIR JOURNEY...

SOON, THEY APPROACHED THE LAKE WHERE MANTHARA, THE TURTLE, LIVED.

WHAT IS THAT ODD CREATURE? IT'S COMING THIS WAY. LET ME HIDE!

NOW, MY FRIEND! HOLD TIGHT. WE'RE GOING DOWN.

WAIT HERE. I'LL GO AND SEE WHERE MANTHARA IS.

MANTHARA! WHERE ARE YOU? MANTHARA! I'M YOUR FRIEND, LAGHUPATANAKA.

THE TURTLE HEARING THE VOICE OF LAGHUPATANAKA CAME OUT OF THE LAKE...

HERE I AM!

THE OLD FRIENDS SPENT SOME TIME TOGETHER HAPPILY.

WHO IS THAT MOUSE?

HIRANYAKA, A GOOD FRIEND OF MINE, WHOSE HEART IS HEAVY WITH SORROW.

I'M DELIGHTED TO SEE YOU, SIR! WHY ARE YOU SO SAD?

IT'S A LONG STORY. IN THE SOUTHERN COUNTRY, THERE IS A CITY...

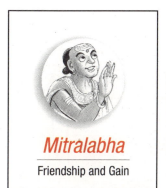

Mitralabha

Friendship and Gain

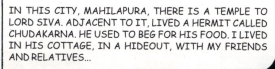

IN THIS CITY, MAHILAPURA, THERE IS A TEMPLE TO LORD SIVA. ADJACENT TO IT, LIVED A HERMIT CALLED CHUDAKARNA. HE USED TO BEG FOR HIS FOOD. I LIVED IN HIS COTTAGE, IN A HIDEOUT, WITH MY FRIENDS AND RELATIVES...

I'LL KEEP THIS FOOD HERE FOR TONIGHT.

COME OUT, MY FRIENDS! HERE'S A FEAST!

HUSH! BE SILENT! FOLLOW ME.

HA! HA! WAH! SO DELICIOUS...

BAVE! BAVE!

OH! THIS IS EMPTY! RATS HAVE EATEN UP MY FOOD!

THE NEXT DAY... I'LL PUT THE FOOD SOMEWHERE ELSE AND FOOL THESE NASTY RATS!

THAT NIGHT...

Mitralabha

Friendship and Gain

HA! HA! FEAST AFTER FEAST FOR US, COMRADES!

THE HERMIT TRIED TO HIDE THE FOOD FROM THE RATS BUT IT WAS IN VAIN.

ONE DAY, A GUEST ARRIVED...

O HOLY SIR, I'M BLESSED BY YOUR VISIT!

CHUDA! GOD BLESS YOU!

THAT NIGHT, AFTER DINNER, THEY ENGAGED IN A DISCUSSION ON PHILOSOPHY. BUT CHUDA-KARNA'S THOUGHTS WERE FIXED ON THE RAT-GANG...

MY DEAR CHUDA! I WONDER HOW ONE CAN GET ETERNAL DELIVERANCE WITHOUT REBIRTH?

EH...YOU MEAN RATS, SIR!

WHAT? WHAT DO YOU MEAN BY "RATS"?

IT'S A PITY YOU'RE TURNING A DEAF EAR TO MY EXPOSITION OF VEDANTA!

BUT...SIR!

NO, YOU DON'T GIVE ME DUE RESPECT. I'M LEAVING YOU THIS VERY NIGHT!

PLEASE EXCUSE ME, SIR! LET ME EXPLAIN TO YOU THE CAUSE OF MY ABSENT-MINDEDNESS!

...THERE...IS...A...WILY RAT... HERE...AND...HE

SO WHAT!

...AND HIS BATTALION INVADE MY PLACE EVERY NIGHT AND DEVOUR MY FOOD WHEREVER I KEEP IT.

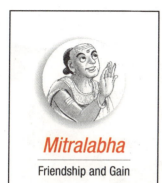

Mitralabha

Friendship and Gain

I DON'T KNOW WHAT TO DO ABOUT THESE RATS, SIR! THAT'S WHY MY BRAIN IS FULL OF THEM.

I'M ON THE LOOK OUT FOR THEIR GANG LEADER, SIR!

HAVE YOU FOUND HIS HIDING-PLACE?

NO, SIR! HE IS TOO CLEVER. AS SOON AS HE SMELLS MY FOOD, HE SNEAKS OUT WITH HIS FRIENDS.

FUNNY! THIS REMINDS ME OF AN INCIDENT!

PLEASE TELL ME!

ONE DAY, WHEN I CAMPED IN A BRAHMIN'S HOUSE, I HEARD THIS...

MY DEAR! TOMORROW, I'LL BE GOING TO THE NEARBY TOWN AS IT IS A HOLY DAY. INVITE AND FEED A BRAHMIN.

WHAT DO WE HAVE? WE DON'T EVEN HAVE ANYTHING FOR OURSELVES!

DON'T TALK LIKE THAT. IT'S VERY BAD! EVEN IF YOU HAVE A MORSEL OF FOOD, GIVE HALF OF IT TO THE DESERVING AT THE RIGHT TIME.

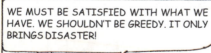

WE MUST BE SATISFIED WITH WHAT WE HAVE. WE SHOULDN'T BE GREEDY. IT ONLY BRINGS DISASTER!

ONCE, A HUNTER SAW A FAT BOAR IN A WOOD...

THAT'S A FINE-LOOKING BOAR! IT WILL MAKE A SUMPTUOUS MEAL.

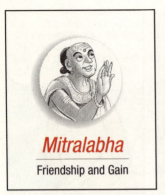

Mitralabha

Friendship and Gain

I MUST BAG THIS ANIMAL!

THE ARROW OF THE HUNTER PIERCED THE BOAR. IN AGONY, THE BOAR ATTACKED THE HUNTER. THE HUNTER AND THE BOAR ENDED UP KILLING EACH OTHER...

MEANWHILE... HAH! HAH! TWO BIRDS AT ONE SHOT! A BOAR AND A MAN!

HOW LUCKY I AM! GOD IS MERCIFUL! HE HAS PROVIDED ME WITH FOOD FOR MONTHS. SURELY, THIS IS THE FRUIT OF MY GOOD DEEDS IN PAST LIVES...THAT IS THE WAY OF FATE!

I'LL EAT THIS FOOD SLOWLY TO MAKE IT LAST LONGER.

THE GREEDY JACKAL BEGAN TO EAT THE BOWSTRING MADE OF GUT. SUDDENLY, THE STRING SNAPPED, HIT THE JACKAL AND KILLED IT...

THE BRAHMIN FINISHED HIS STORY THUS:

AND THAT'S HOW THE GREEDY JACKAL PERISHED...

ON THE FACE OF EVERY LIVING BEING, HIS FATE IS WRITTEN, EVEN BEFORE HE IS BORN...

HIS LIFE, WEALTH, FORTUNE AND THE PLACE OF DEATH--ALL ARE PREDETERMINED.

ALL RIGHT! I'LL FEED A BRAHMIN.

SO THE BRAHMIN'S WIFE CLEANED A BOWL OF RICE AND KEPT IT ASIDE.. BUT AS LUCK WOULD HAVE IT, A DOG TOUCHED IT...

WHAT BAD LUCK! WHAT WILL I DO?

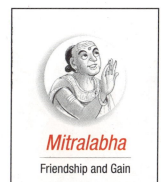

Mitralabha

Friendship and Gain

THIS RICE IS POLLUTED. I'D BETTER EXCHANGE IT WITH SOMEONE.

SHE WENT TO A NEIGHBOUR...

ALL RIGHT! TAKE THIS PADDY IN EXCHANGE FOR YOUR RICE.

I'VE MADE A GOOD BARGAIN TODAY IN EXCHANGING PADDY FOR RICE!

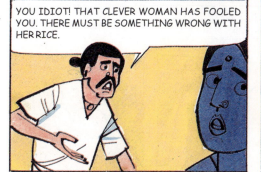

YOU IDIOT! THAT CLEVER WOMAN HAS FOOLED YOU. THERE MUST BE SOMETHING WRONG WITH HER RICE.

THROW IT AWAY AT ONCE!

THE HOLY MAN CONCLUDED HIS STORY:

CHUDA! EVERY ACTION HAS A REASON BEHIND IT.

LET'S FIND OUT THE HIDING-PLACE OF THE RATS IN THE MORNING AND DESTROY IT FORTHWITH. DELAY IS ALWAYS DANGEROUS.

HIRANYAKA WENT ON WITH HIS STORY TO LAGHUPATANA KA, THE CROW, AND MANTHARA, THE TURTLE...

WHEN I OVERHEARD THEIR CONVERSATION, I WAS AFRAID THAT THEY WOULD DISCOVER MY HIDE-OUT.

THEN WHAT DID YOU DO?

WHAT A CRITICAL SITUATION!

SO, I WARNED MY FOLLOWERS ABOUT THE IMPENDING DANGER AND WE FLED FROM THE PLACE IN UTTER PANIC.

HIRANYAKA, WHERE ARE YOU TAKING US? THIS PATH IS NEW TO US.

Mitralabha

Friendship and Gain

14

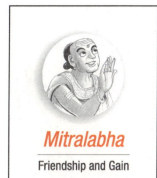

Mitralabha

Friendship and Gain

IN THIS WORLD, SOMEONE WHO POSSESSES WEALTH IS CONSIDERED STRONG, WISE, WITTY, AND SO ON. BUT...

...WHEN HE LOSES IT, HE BECOMES A NOBODY.

HOW DARE HE SAY SUCH THINGS! I MUST SHOW THEM MY STRENGTH NOW.

HIRANYAKA TRIED TO JUMP AND SNATCH THE RICE BOWL BUT HE FELL FLAT ON HIS FACE...

HAHHA! HAHA! LOOK, LOOK! DIDN'T I TELL YOU THAT HE WOULD LOSE HIS STRENGTH ALONG WITH HIS TREASURE?

HA-HA! YES, SIR!

HO! I'M RUINED. I'VE LOST MY STRENGTH. NOW I'M A PAUPER.

LET'S LEAVE THIS FELLOW. HE CAN'T FEED US ANY MORE.

WAIT! PLEASE LISTEN.

WHO WANTS YOUR STORIES? YOU'RE AN IDIOT.

THE POOR HAVE THEIR OWN VIRTUES BUT THEY WON'T SHINE. TRUE, TRUE!

WHEN SOMEONE IS POOR EVEN HIS KITH AND KIN WILL INSULT HIM.

WHEN ONE IS POOR, EVEN THE BEST OF ONE'S FRIENDS TURN INTO ENEMIES.

Mitralabha

Friendship and Gain

I'VE NOTHING TO DO HERE EXCEPT GO BACK TO THE FOREST.

AFTER SOME TIME...

OH! WHAT AM I TO DO? AM I TO GO A-BEGGING?

NO! WHAT ABOUT MY PRESTIGE? NO...NO!

HOW SHALL I KEEP MYSELF ALIVE? WHY NOT TAKE TO ROBBERY?

NO!...NO. IT'S BETTER TO DIE THAN BECOME A ROBBER.

THERE IS ONLY ONE WAY LEFT. I MUST GET BACK MY TREASURE FROM CHUDAKARNA, **I MUST!**

SO I TRIED TO GET BACK MY TREASURE BUT THAT VILLAIN HIT ME WITH HIS STICK.

THEN, WHAT HAPPENED?

NOTHING. I REALIZED THAT WE GET WHAT WE DESERVE.

THIS REMINDS ME OF A STORY.

ONCE, A MERCHANT'S SON BOUGHT A BOOK FOR 200 GOLD PIECES...

MY SON! WHAT DID YOU DO WITH THE MONEY?

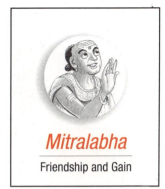

Mitralabha

Friendship and Gain

YOU FOOL! YOU BOUGHT THIS USELESS BOOK FOR TWO HUNDRED GOLD PIECES?

YES, FATHER!

YOU DON'T KNOW THE VALUE OF MONEY!

PLEASE DON'T SAY THAT. THIS IS A VERY PRECIOUS BOOK WITH A VALUABLE SAYING IN IT:"WE GET ONLY WHAT WE DESERVE."

YOU SQUANDERED TWO HUNDRED GOLD PIECES ON THIS FOOLISH SAYING? YOU DON'T DESERVE TO LIVE IN MY HOUSE!

GET OUT! FROM NOW ON, MAKE YOUR OWN LIVING!

SO THE MERCHANT'S SON LEFT HOME AND TRAVELLED TILL HE CAME TO A CITY. THERE, A FRIEND SAW HIM WANDERING ABOUT...

WHAT HAS BROUGHT YOU TO THIS DISTANT LAND, MY FRIEND?

WE GET ONLY WHAT WE DESERVE.

POOR FELLOW! HE'S GONE CRAZY.

THAT NIGHT, THE MERCHANT'S SON WAS WANDERING ABOUT WHEN THE PRINCESS SAW HIM. IN THE DARK, SHE MISTOOK HIM FOR HER LOVER...

COME ON... CLIMB UP!

WHY IS SHE ASKING ME TO COME UP?

WHY DO YOU HESITATE? HURRY UP!

Mitralabha

Friendship and Gain

I'VE BEEN WAITING FOR YOU A LONG TIME...I LOVE YOU SO MUCH.

LET'S GO INSIDE!

IN THE LIGHT, THE PRINCESS SAW THE STRANGER'S FACE...

HO! WHO ARE YOU?

WE ONLY GET WHAT WE DESERVE.

YOU...GET OUT OF MY SIGHT!

THE MERCHANT'S SON LEFT THE PRINCESS AND ONCE AGAIN ROAMED ABOUT THE STREETS. A MARRIAGE PROCESSION WENT PAST...

WHY NOT FOLLOW THIS PROCESSION?

MEANWHILE...

OH, MY GOD! A MAD ELEPHANT!

RUN FOR YOUR LIFE!

DON'T BE AFRAID...NO HARM WILL COME TO YOU!

THANK YOU!

YOU MAD CREATURE! IS NOT LIFE SWEET TO YOU? GET AWAY FROM HERE!

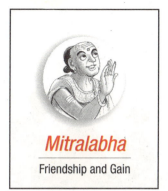

Mitralabha

Friendship and Gain

THE MAD ELEPHANT TURNED AROUND AND WENT AWAY. IT SEEMED FATE HAD PLAYED A TRICK! AT THIS MOMENT, THE BRIDEGROOM AND HIS PARTY CAME TO THE SPOT WHERE THE BRIDE WAS STANDING...

WHAT IS GOING ON? WHO'S THIS FELLOW HOLDING YOUR HAND?

HE SAVED MY LIFE...ONLY HE DESERVES TO MARRY ME!

MEANWHILE, THE BRIDE'S FATHER ARRIVED...

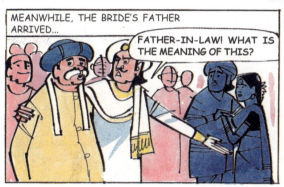

FATHER-IN-LAW! WHAT IS THE MEANING OF THIS?

MY DEAR, WHAT ARE YOU DOING?

HE SAVED ME FROM THAT MAD ELEPHANT. ONLY HE DESERVES MY HAND.

WE ONLY GET WHAT WE DESERVE!

MEANWHILE, THE KING AND THE PRINCESS CAME THAT WAY...

WHAT IS THIS COMMOTION?

THEN THEY TOLD HIM WHAT HAD HAPPENED...

SO...HE'S THE MAN WHO DROVE THAT WILD ELEPHANT AWAY?

THEN HE DESERVES MY DAUGHTER'S HAND, TOO!

WE ONLY GET WHAT WE DESERVE!

Mitralabha

Friendship and Gain

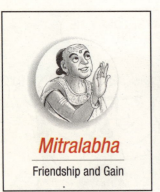

HIRANYAKA CONCLUDED HIS STORY...

SO THE MERCHANT'S SON MARRIED THE PRINCESS, BECAME THE KING, AND LIVED HAPPILY EVER AFTER...

NOW YOU SEE? WE ONLY GET WHAT WE DESERVE.

SO I REALISED THAT MONEY IS NOT THE ONLY WORTHY POSSESSION. ONE SHOULD HAVE CHARACTER, WISDOM AND CONTENTMENT.

THAT'S MY STORY. IT WAS THEN THAT LAGHUPATANAKA AND I MET. THEN I DECIDED TO COME WITH HIM TO YOUR PLACE!

MY FRIEND! WHY ARE YOU DEPRESSED BECAUSE YOU'RE IN A STRANGE LAND? FOR AN INTELLIGENT AND BRAVE PERSON LIKE YOU, EVERY PLACE IS HOME.

IT IS ALL FATE'S DOING. A KING MAY BECOME A BEGGAR AND A BEGGAR MAY BECOME A KING. A BRAVE MAN MAY BE SLAIN BY A COWARD...

IF ONE HAS DETERMINATION, THEN EVEN MOUNT KAILASH IS NOT TOO HIGH OR THE MIGHTY OCEAN ENDLESS...

I KNOW THAT YOUR PURSE IS LEAN BUT YOU HAVE BRAINS AND ENERGY. SO WHY WORRY?

CONTENTMENT IS TRUE WEALTH. THIS REMINDS ME OF THE STORY OF THE WEAVER.

ONCE UPON A TIME, THERE LIVED A WEAVER...

I DON'T KNOW WHY I'M UNABLE TO MAKE MONEY LIKE OTHER WEAVERS EVEN THOUGH MY FABRICS ARE FINER THAN THEIRS!

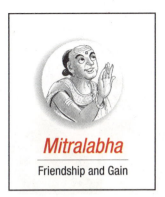

Mitralabha

Friendship and Gain

MY DEAR, I'M FED UP WITH THIS PLACE. I WANT TO GO TO ANOTHER TOWN AND TRY MY LUCK THERE.

A CHANGE OF PLACE DOESN'T CHANGE YOUR LUCK. WHAT IS ORDAINED BY FATE WILL HAPPEN.

YOU'RE WRONG, MY DEAR! IF YOU DON'T TRY, YOU CAN'T ACHIEVE A THING.

THE WEAVER THEN WENT TO THE CITY OF VARDHAMANAPURA AND STAYED THERE FOR SOME TIME.

I'VE SAVED ENOUGH MONEY. IT'S TIME TO GO BACK HOME.

ON HIS WAY...

IT'S MIDNIGHT. I'LL REST UNDER THIS TREE FOR A WHILE.

AFTER A FEW MINUTES, THE WEAVER SLEPT. HE BEGAN DREAMING...

DEAR KARTHA, YOU NEVER ALLOWED THIS WEAVER TO SAVE IN HIS LIFETIME. BUT NOW HE HAS THREE HUNDRED GOLD PIECES. HOW DID IT HAPPEN?

DEAR KRIYA, I LET HIM SAVE THAT MUCH BECAUSE OF HIS EFFORT. IF YOU THINK IT'S NOT RIGHT, TAKE IT AWAY.

SUDDENLY, THE WEAVER WOKE UP...

GONE! MY GOD! WHERE IS MY GOLD? THIS IS EMPTY!

Mitralabha

Friendship and Gain

HOW CAN I GO BACK HOME WITH EMPTY HANDS! ALL MY LABOUR IS WASTED.

SO THE WEAVER WENT BACK TO VARDHAMANAPURA, WORKED HARD FOR SOME MONTHS, EARNED FIVE HUNDRED GOLD PIECES AND STARTED HOME AGAIN...

ON HIS WAY...

I'M EXHAUSTED. I'LL REST FOR A WHILE UNDER THIS TREE.

AFTER SOME TIME, HE FELL ASLEEP AND STARTED DREAMING...

KARTHA! HOW COULD THIS WEAVER SAVE THIS GOLD AGAIN?

HARD WORK AND ENTERPRISE MUST HAVE THEIR REWARD. BUT YOU SHOULD DECIDE HIS FATE.

AND THEN THE WEAVER WOKE UP.

OH! OH! OH! IT IS GONE AGAIN!

THE FRUIT OF CEASELESS TOIL IS GONE!

I SHALL PUT AN END TO THIS WRETCHED LIFE.

THE DEJECTED WEAVER TRIED TO HANG HIMSELF.

STOP! STOP!

DON'T BE HASTY!

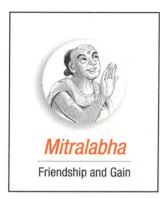

Mitralabha

Friendship and Gain

DON'T PUT AN END TO YOUR LIFE. IT IS I WHO TOOK YOUR SAVINGS!

I CAN'T ALLOW YOU TO HAVE MORE THAN WHAT YOU NEED FOR FOOD AND CLOTHING.

HOWEVER, LET ME KNOW YOUR WISH AND I'LL GRANT IT.

THEN GIVE ME LOTS OF MONEY!

WHAT'S THE USE, WHEN YOU NEITHER ENJOY IT NOR GIVE IT AWAY AS CHARITY?

I WANT IT BECAUSE A RICH MAN IS RESPECTED EVEN IF HE'S A MISER.

GO BACK, THEN, TO VARDHAMANAPURA. TWO PEOPLE NAMED LOBHI AND VYAYASILA LIVE THERE...

GO TO THEIR HOUSES AND WATCH THEM. YOU WILL KNOW THE VALUE OF MONEY.

THE WEAVER ONCE AGAIN RETURNED TO VARDHAMANAPURA AND WENT TO LOBHI'S HOUSE.

SIR, I'M A STRANGER TO THIS PLACE. MAY I STAY HERE FOR THE NIGHT?

YES!

WHO IS THIS FELLOW? WHY HAVE YOU ALLOWED HIM TO STAY?

Mitralabha

Friendship and Gain

WHO IS GOING TO COOK FOR HIM AND FEED HIM?

LATER...

THEY COULDN'T HELP GIVING ME SOMETHING TO EAT BUT THEY DID NOT UTTER ONE KIND WORD.

THEY QUARREL FOR NOTHING. LET ME GO TO THE OTHER FELLOW, VYAYASILA.

WELCOME, SIR! I'M HONOURED BY YOUR VISIT.

THANK YOU!

MAKE YOURSELF COMFORTABLE. TREAT THIS LIKE YOUR HOME.

VYAYASILA IS POORER THAN LOBHI. YET HOW KIND AND HOSPITABLE HE IS!

THEN THE WEAVER RETURNED TO HIS NATIVE TOWN.

PLEASE GRANT ME THIS BOON! LET ME LIVE LIKE VYAYASILA.

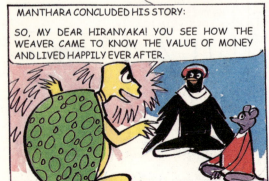

MANTHARA CONCLUDED HIS STORY:

SO, MY DEAR HIRANYAKA! YOU SEE HOW THE WEAVER CAME TO KNOW THE VALUE OF MONEY AND LIVED HAPPILY EVER AFTER.

YOU'LL LOSE ALL YOUR WEALTH IF FATE SO DECREES. NO ONE CAN ALTER FATE.

THIS REMINDS ME OF AN INTERESTING STORY. ONCE, A SNAKE WAS HELD CAPTIVE IN A BASKET.

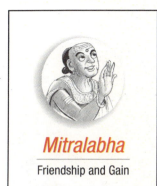

Mitralabha

Friendship and Gain

THOUGHT THE SNAKE TO ITSELF:

I'M STARVING HERE. I'M SURE TO DIE IN THIS DUNGEON.

THEN...

WONDER WHAT THIS BASKET CONTAINS?

THERE MAY BE SOMETHING TO EAT IN IT!

I'LL SEE!

THE MOUSE MADE A HOLE AND CRAWLED INTO THE BASKET...

IT'S VERY DARK INSIDE!

THE HUNGRY SNAKE CAUGHT THE MOUSE SWALLOWED IT UP.

YOU SEE NOW HOW MYSTERIOUS FATE IS. THE SNAKE ESCAPED THROUGH THE HOLE WHICH HAD BEEN MADE BY THE MOUSE.

MY DEAR MANTHARA, YOU HAVE CHANGED MY MIND. I'VE NO WORRY NOW ABOUT MONEY.

MY DEAR FRIEND, LET ME ALSO THANK YOU FOR THE GOOD ADVICE YOU'VE GIVEN HIRANYAKA. YOU'VE EASED HIS SORROW...

AT THIS MOMENT, A DEER NAMED CHITRANGA CAME RUNNING THAT WAY...

SOMEBODY IS COMING THIS WAY! LET'S HIDE.

I'LL JUMP INTO THE LAKE BEFORE IT'S TOO LATE.

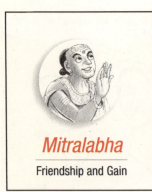

Mitralabha

Friendship and Gain

THE MOUSE, THE CROW AND THE TURTLE HID THEMSELVES IN DIFFERENT PLACES. AFTER SOME TIME...

MY FRIENDS! COME OUT...THERE'S NO CAUSE FOR ALARM...IT'S ONLY A DEER.

DEAR FELLOW! WHY, YOU ARE TREMBLING! WHAT ARE YOU AFRAID OF?

FIRST, DRINK SOME WATER.

I'M BEING CHASED BY HUNTERS. THEY'RE AFTER ME. I ESCAPED AND CAME HERE!

I NEED YOUR ASSISTANCE.

WHAT IS THE GOOD OF MAKING FRIENDS WITH TINY CREATURES LIKE US?

DON'T SAY THAT. DON'T YOU KNOW THE STORY OF THE MICE THAT HELPED THE ELEPHANTS?

PLEASE TELL US THE STORY!

THERE WAS ONCE A LARGE COMMUNITY OF MICE WHICH LIVED HAPPILY IN THE DILAPIDATED HOUSES OF AN OLD RUINED CITY.

ONE DAY...

MY GOD! A HUGE HERD OF ELEPHANTS!

THEY'RE COMING THIS WAY. WE'RE FINISHED!

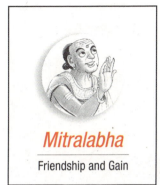

Mitralabha

Friendship and Gain

HO! RUN! HO! HO!

ELEPHANTS!

THOUSANDS OF MICE WERE CRUSHED TO DEATH BY THE ELEPHANTS ON THEIR WAY TO A NEARBY LAKE...

AFTER SOME TIME...

MY FRIENDS, A TERRIBLE DISASTER HAS BEFALLEN US. BUT IT'S NO USE CRYING. WE MUST DO SOMETHING.

THE ELEPHANTS WILL SOON RETURN FROM THE LAKE. WE MUST DO SOMETHING.

THE MICE SENT A DELEGATION TO THE KING OF THE ELEPHANTS.

O MIGHTY KING! WE LIVE IN THE TOWN NEARBY...

THOUSANDS OF MICE WERE CRUSHED TO DEATH BY YOU ON THE WAY TO THE LAKE.

IF YOU RETURN THE SAME WAY, NOT ONE MOUSE WILL BE LEFT ALIVE.

BE MERCIFUL AND SPARE US. WE'LL BE OF USE TO YOU SOME DAY.

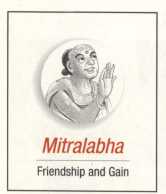

Mitralabha

Friendship and Gain

ALL RIGHT! WE WON'T COME THAT WAY. YOU CAN GO.

SOME TIME PASSED. THE ELEPHANT KING AND SEVERAL OF HIS ATTENDANTS WERE TRAPPED BY THE HUNTERS OF THE KING.

WHO CAN FREE US?

AH! I'LL SEND A MESSENGER TO THE MICE.

IN THE TOWN WHERE THE MICE LIVED...

I'VE COME TO SEEK YOUR HELP!

OUR HELP?

YES. OUR KING AND SOME OF HIS FOLLOWERS HAVE BEEN TRAPPED.

WE'RE ALWAYS READY TO HELP OUR FRIENDS.

CHITRANGA BROUGHT THE STORY TO AN END...

THE MICE RAN TO THE RESCUE OF THE ELEPHANTS, CHEWED UP THE ROPES THAT BOUND THEM, AND SET THEM FREE. I THEREFORE SAY: MAKE FRIENDS WITH EVERYBODY.

WE AGREE WITH YOU. FROM NOW ON, WE'RE FRIENDS. YOU'RE ONE OF US.

SO THE FOUR FRIENDS LIVED HAPPILY TOGETHER. ONE DAY...

WHERE IS OUR FRIEND, CHITRANGA? WE'VE NOT SEEN HIM FOR SOME TIME.

Mitralabha

Friendship and Gain

I'M AFRAID CHITRANGA MAY BE IN TROUBLE.

DEAR LAGHUPATANAKA, PLEASE GO LOOK FOR HIM!

SO LAGHUPATANAKA FLEW OFF IN SEARCH OF THEIR FRIEND.

AFTER SOME TIME...

THERE HE IS! HE'S BEEN TRAPPED BY A HUNTER.

DEAR FRIEND! HOW DID THIS HAPPEN?

WHAT CAN I SAY? IT'S MY FATE!

BREAK MY BONDS AND RELEASE ME QUICKLY BEFORE THE HUNTER RETURNS!

HAVE NO FEAR WHEN YOU'VE FRIENDS LIKE US! I'LL BRING HIRANYAKA IN NO TIME. HE CAN SET YOU FREE.

THEN LAGHUPATA-NAKA RETURNED TO HIS FRIENDS AND TOLD THEM ABOUT CHITRANGA BEING TRAPPED.

HURRY UP! TIME IS SHORT. I'LL CARRY YOU ON MY BACK!

Mitralabha

Friendship and Gain

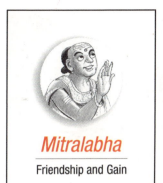

Mitralabha

Friendship and Gain

OH, NO! HE'S AFTER ME!

AHA! AHA!

YOU'LL BE SAFE HERE.

WHAT TERRIBLE LUCK! I'VE FREED ONE FRIEND. NOW ANOTHER ONE IS TRAPPED!

THERE ARE MANY FALSE FRIENDS AND TOO MANY RELATIVES. ONLY A TRUE FRIEND HELPS US IN TIMES OF DANGER.

LOSING A FRIEND IS LIKE DEATH...

MEANWHILE...

OH, POOR MANTHARA! GREAT MISFORTUNE HAS BEFALLEN US!

AS LONG AS MANTHARA IS WITHIN SIGHT, WE'VE A CHANCE TO SAVE HIM. NOW, MY PLAN.

LATER...

ANOTHER DEER! I'M IN LUCK!

THE HUNTER THREW THE TURTLE ON THE GROUND AND RAN TOWARDS THE DEER...

HE'S COMING CLOSE! WE HAVE TO ACT QUICKLY! LIE DOWN LIKE A CORPSE AND I'LL PECK AT YOU...

SUDDENLY...

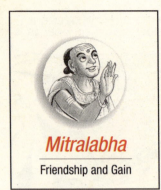

Mitralabha
Friendship and Gain

THEN THE DEER, NONE OTHER THAN CHITRANGA, GOT UP, AND WITH LIGHTNING SPEED SWEPT INTO THE WOODS. THE CROW, NONE OTHER THAN LAGHUPATANAKA, FLEW AWAY...

HIRANYAKA! HOW...DID YOU...?

HUSH! I'LL SET YOU FREE. JUMP INTO THAT LAKE. QUICK!

NOW YOU'RE SAFE, MY FRIEND!

WHAT IS GOING ON? WHERE ARE THE DEER AND THE CROW?

MY GOD! THE TURTLE HAS ALSO DISAPPEARED!

THE WHOLE THING LOOKS FANTASTIC. I'D BETTER GET OUT OF HERE QUICKLY!

VISHNU SHARMA HAD COME TO THE END OF MITRALABHA, THE SECOND PART OF THE PANCHATANRA.

MY DEAR PRINCES! YOU SEE HOW THE FOUR WISE AND LEARNED FRIENDS OVERCAME ALL DIFFICULTIES BY STANDING TOGETHER THOUGH THEIR MEANS WERE LIMITED...

THEY ACHIEVED THEIR PURPOSE AND LIVED HAPPILY EVER AFTER.

NOW WOULD YOU LIKE TO LISTEN TO SANDHI VIGRAHA, THE THIRD PART OF THE PANCHATANTRA? IT DEALS WITH WAR AND PEACE.

PRAY, TELL US THIS STORY!

ONCE, DEEP IN A FOREST, FLOURISHED A GREAT BANYAN TREE. ON THAT TREE LIVED MEGHAVARNA, THE KING OF CROWS...